Blue Heart
Published in Great Britain in 2024 by Graffeg Limited.

Text and illustrations by Nicola Davies copyright ©
2024. Produced by Graffeg Limited copyright © 2024.

Graffeg Limited, 24 Stradey Park Business
Centre, Mwrwg Road, Llangennech, Llanelli,
Carmarthenshire, SA14 8YP, Wales, UK.
www.graffeg.com.

Nicola Davies is hereby identified as the author of this
work in accordance with section 77 of the Copyright,
Designs and Patents Act 1988.

A CIP Catalogue record for this book is available
from the British Library.

ISBN 9781802587500

1 2 3 4 5 6 7 8 9

FSC
www.fsc.org

MIX
Paper from
responsible sources
FSC® C014138

BLUE HEART

Nicola Davies

Words and Illustrations about Whales

Foreword *Dr Helen Scales*

One of my favourite ocean treasures, part of a messy collection of things that I've found and that people have given me over the years, is the fossilised ear bone of an ancient sperm whale.

The stone is shaped like a thick-lipped, broken cup and makes for a satisfying, heavy handful. It was a gift from a friend who found it while scuba diving in a muddy river in the United States after it washed from a mountain rock that used to be seabed. Whoever holds the petrified bone is transported back more than ten million years, to the time when the animal this belonged to was listening carefully for echoes resonating through the ocean as they searched for prey.

I especially like this fossil because it reminds me that whales were once land-walkers, then they went back to the ocean and rejoined their swimming ancestors. The proto-whales' bodies became adapted once again for aquatic life, including a chunky ear bone, all the better for detecting sounds underwater.

I've been lucky enough to catch glimpses of living sperm whales in the wild, with their unmistakable square noses and vapour spouts that shoot sideways into the sky from their single nostril (the other closed off and became part of their internal, sound-making anatomy). I gasped as the sperm whales leapt clear of the sea before plunging into the twilight zone of the deep ocean to hunt for squid.

You can't plan to meet a wild whale. The vast ocean is their home and they are free to go anywhere they please. Every encounter is a moment to hold dear, when you and they happen to be in the same place at the same time, or when you find yourself within earshot of their songs. There are times and places where you stand a better chance of crossing paths with a great cetacean, and there are tools scientists use to listen out for them and follow their migrations.

Ultimately, though, to see a whale requires a happy coincidence — a fluke, if you like.

Nicola Davies has seen more whales than most of us and she shares many of those breathtaking, thought-provoking moments in this stunning collection of words, pictures, reflections and stories. She shows us how human connections with great whales are complicated and inconstant; over time, people have changed their minds about what they are for, why they matter and how they should be treated.

In the past, whales were little more than an industrial resource there for the taking, until more and more people embraced them as glorious wildlife and deemed them worthy of reverence and protection. Most of all, as *Blue Heart* shows us so brilliantly, whales are a tremendous gift of the ocean, and we must not take them for granted but continue to treasure them, know them and care about them. The biggest animals ever to exist have proven they are tough and resilient and are now returning in greater numbers, proving that our wounded ocean can heal if given a chance. The beauty and wonder of whales gives us reason to be hopeful and to keep fighting for a better future.

Dr Helen Scales

Blue Heart *Nicola Davies*

I've always adored the sea. I'd stay in the waves as a child until I was blue with cold and crinkly from immersion. And I've always loved animals, but growing up in the UK, birds are mostly what I saw, so birds became what I wanted to concentrate on when I went to Cambridge to study zoology.

This changed when I, quite literally, bumped into a young man who went on to be the foremost whale scientist of his generation, Hal Whitehead. Hal (now Professor Whitehead) was looking for a research assistant for a study of humpback whales off the coast of Newfoundland, and I got the job. I spent two summers watching humpbacks from cliffs and the decks of Hal's small boat, *Firenze*, and I was hooked. Thanks in large part to Hal and his wide network of colleagues, over the many years since I've spent time on other small boats, helping with studies of blue whales and sperm whales, in Sri Lanka, the Sea of Cortez in Mexico and in Dominica in the Caribbean. I've spent many days staring at the blue horizon all around looking for whale blows, balancing data sheets on my lap as shipmates shout observations and measurements about huge groups of sperm whales. I've got good at scooping whale poo and whale skin from the sea and at fixing humpback whale positions from a cliff using a surveyor's transit. I've never got good at being a sailor, however, as I've always been too busy being lost in the wonder of the ocean and being, forever, seasick. Outside of scientific studies, I've also seen whales in Alaska, South Africa, Spitzbergen, the Azores and here at home in Pembrokeshire, although here we see mostly smaller members of the cetacean clan, common dolphins and porpoises.

I've tried to share my passion for whales and the sea with the children and adults I've written for and worked with. My very first book for children, published over 25 years ago, was a picture book about blue whales. I must have paced out the length of a blue whale in hundreds of school halls across the UK and around the world. In 2023 I saw blue whales for the first time in more than a decade from the decks of a whale watching ship in the Azores – a mother and a baby looking exactly like the wonderful illustration (by Nick Malland) in that first book. It felt like a very special sort of completion. I have a sense of circles closing in my relationship to humpback whales too; they were my first whales, but although I've taught thousands of children how to make the basic sounds of humpback song, it took me until 2023 to write a book about it.

I've put whales into both non-fiction books and fantasy novels. This book isn't fantasy, but it isn't quite non-fiction either, although it will give you some factual information about whales. It is a celebration in pictures and poems of some of the species of whales I've seen and spent time with. It is a very personal collection, as although it reflects some of the biology of these wondrous creatures, it is mostly about my experiences of them, and the deep and lasting impression they have made on me. I suppose you could say it's an extended love letter.

Whales are perhaps a hundred times less numerous now than they once were before humans began to hunt them. Even though large-scale commercial whaling has ended, whales face terrible threats from our activities, collisions with shipping, entanglement in fishing gear, pollution, climate change and the erosion of their food sources through overfishing. I know that I am incredibly lucky to have seen a whale at all and that it is an experience that a vanishingly tiny percentage of humanity can hope to have. But if we humans make the right decisions, in the future whales might not be so hard to see as they are now. There is a growing recognition of the vital role that whales play in regulating the balance of our atmosphere, and as a result, our climate. They are nutrient recyclers, bringing nourishment from the depths to promote the growth of plant plankton in the sunlit upper reaches of the oceans that produce half of the oxygen in our atmosphere. They also store up carbon in their bodies and keep it locked in the depths of the sea when they die and sink to the bottom. Recent studies suggest that if we were to restore whale populations to what they were before humans began commercial whaling, whales could take 1.7 billion tons of CO_2 from the atmosphere every year, equivalent to the emissions produced by all the cars in the USA.

But there is more to whales than 'ecosystem services'. Seeing a wild whale is an experience that touches every kind of heart. It reminds us that as human beings we share in the joy and wonder of the natural world and that we all belong here on this beautiful planet. I believe that the goal of mending our beleaguered Earth, through restoring whale populations and all wild ecosystems, in the sea and on the land, could unite humankind and allow us to become a better version of ourselves, compassionate to all life, caring of all our fellow beings.

Nicola Davies

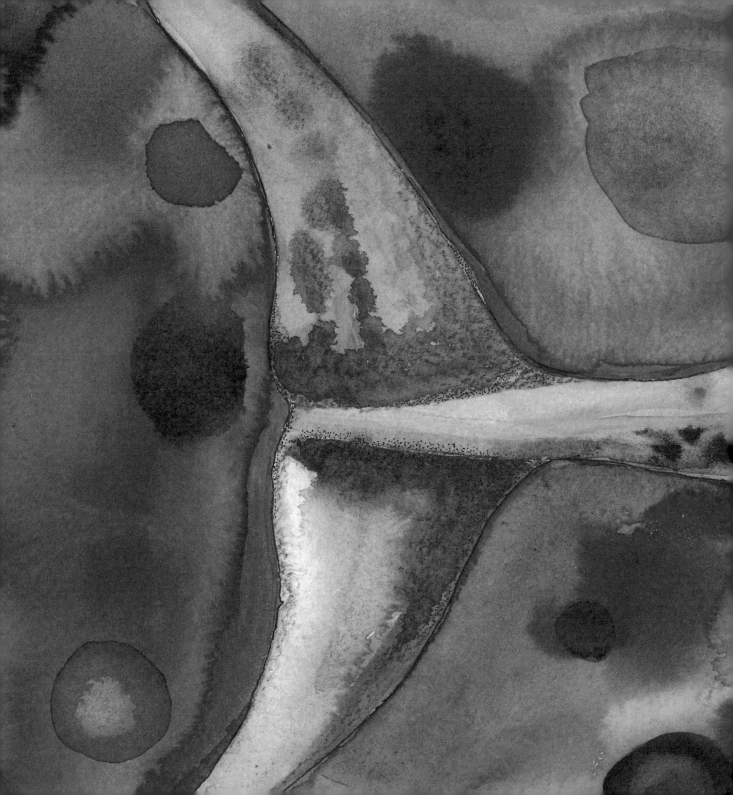

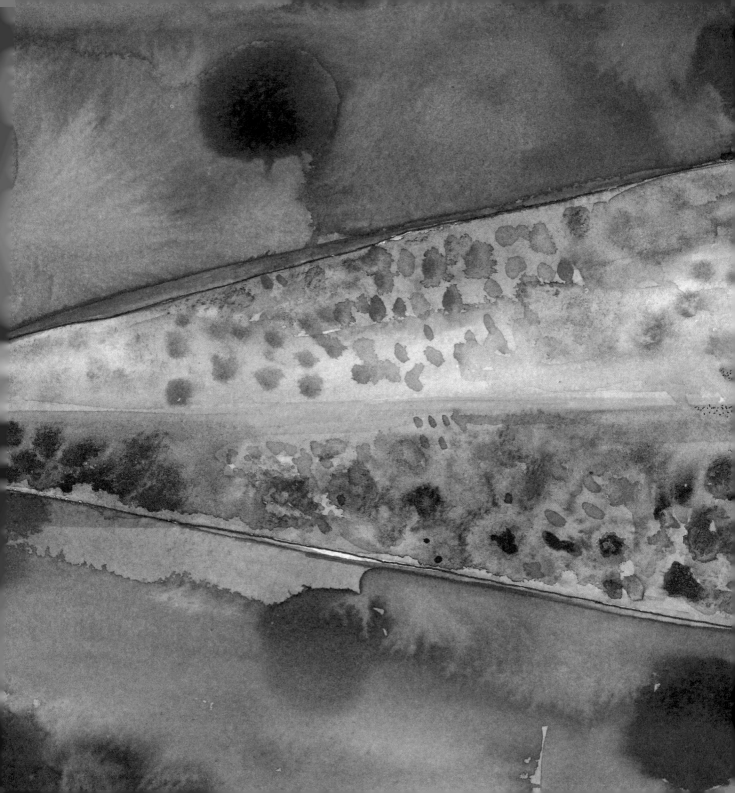

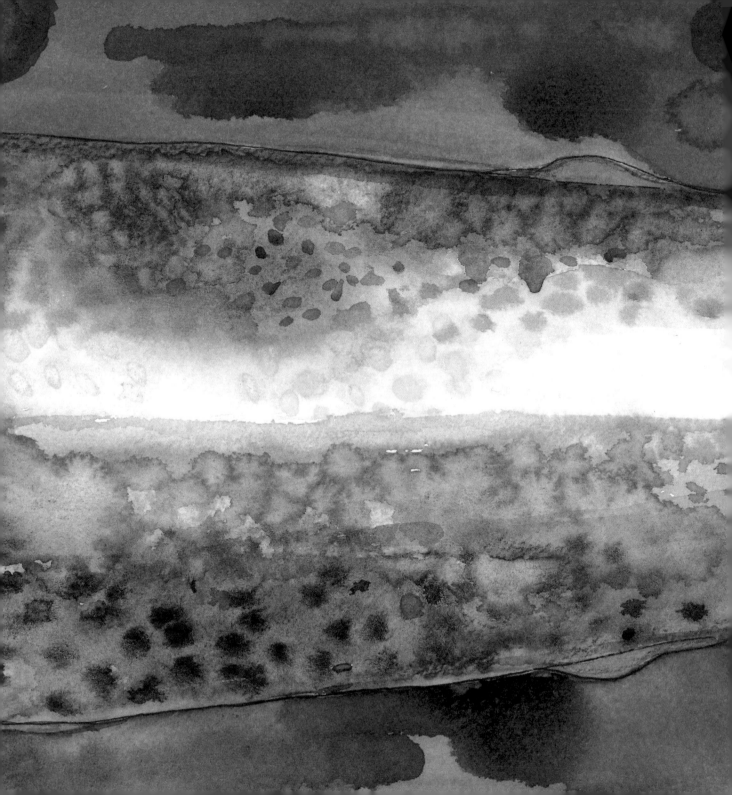

Blue Whales

Blue whales are not only the biggest animals on earth now, they are the biggest animals that have ever lived.

Their huge size allows them to wander enormous distances in search of the dense patches of shrimp-like creatures and shoals of small fish on which they depend. But this vagabond lifestyle has a cost – it means that individuals are often separated by hundreds or thousands of miles of ocean, making it tricky when it comes to breeding season. Blue whales get round this by producing low humming sounds, a frequency perfect for long-distance propagation through the sea. Before humans made so much noise in the seas, a blue whale off Hawaii could probably say 'Hi' to a blue whale in the Ross Sea off Antarctica. When you hear this sound it is like a vast engine thrumming in the deep, a sound you feel in you body rather than hear with your ears. It conveys the sheer scale of the animal almost more than seeing its endlessly long back slipping through the water, or watching its great flukes rise up, then vanish.

Blue Heart

If you look at Earth from space it isn't green,
You can't see trees and grass from way up there,
Nor the paintbox brown of deserts that they put on maps;
The twinkly, sequin-scatter of our city lights fades out too,
The colour of our planet is just blue.

If you cut me open you'd see the usual stuff,
Red blood, white bone, the porridge grey of brain,
Thirty trillion cells in singing tangle, each cell a tiny sea,
A minute memory of the ocean where first it grew,
And in the middle of them all, my heart is blue.

One day perhaps we'll learn to play amongst the stars
To bathe in the phosphorescent glow of galaxies
And wander to the very edge of time.
But we'll never quite forget this life we knew,
Home always and forever will be blue.

How Big is a Blue Whale?

From the start I could quote the stats;
A body as long as three school buses,
The slow...
wait for it
wait   for   it
wait   for   it
BEAT
of a heart the size of a small car,
an aorta you could post a toddler down.
But I did not really really understand
that humongous, huge, enormous, vast
don't work for creatures more like landscape than like living thing.
Until
Until
the fluke lifted from the ocean, big as weather,
swept down,
casual as God-turning-over-in-bed-to-make-the-Himalayas,
and almost sank our boat.
Until
I heard the blow
like a door opening in a cathedral
or a stone dropping down into a cavern that could swallow Paris.
Then at last I knew
how big   BIG   BIG
a blue whale really is.

Respect the Invisible

Oxygen's invisible, but right now your body's busy with it:
the hidden space inside your lungs (bigger than your living room)
extracting it with every breath;
blood vessels, long enough to loop the world five times,
deliver it to every part.
You don't have to think about it.
It's all invisible to your conscious mind.

Whales are invisible too.
You don't see them in the ordinary world of living rooms.
They are off somewhere at the edges of imagination, almost fictional.
And yet your every breath connects you to a whale.
Whales fertilise the sunny upper reaches of the ocean
so the plants there – also almost invisible – flourish,
and make half the oxygen you breathe.

You should pay attention to things that are invisible
Especially the ones on which your life depends.

Not only does whale activity put oxygen into the atmosphere, it takes carbon dioxide out. Restoring whale populations to pre-whaling levels would be a powerful weapon against climate change.

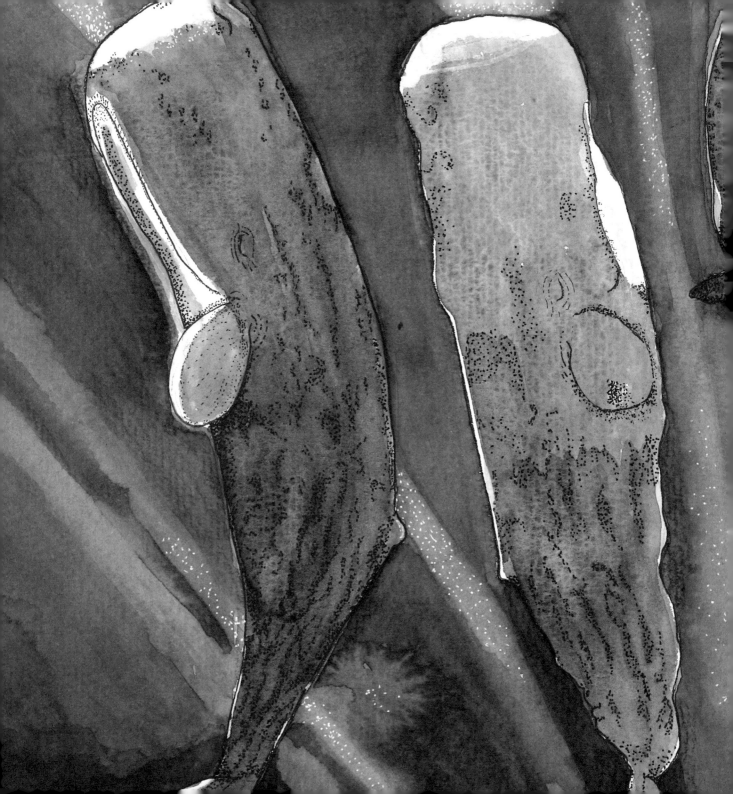

Sperm Whales

Although sperm whales are big and are classed as great whales, they belong to the same group as orca, the odontocetes, or toothed whales.

They catch prey individually, rather than gulping millions all at once, as baleen whales (blues, humpbacks and right whales) do. Sperm whales hunt in depths of over 1,000m and find their prey in total darkness using the sophisticated echolocation system in their huge, square heads. Their echolocation clicks are a useful way for researchers to locate sperm whales when they are on long dives lasting up to an hour. Sperm whales are highly social, with females forming stable groups, visited from time to time by the huge, and largely solitary, males. Scientists are slowly deciphering their communication clicks, called codas, so one day we may be able to understand what they're saying.

Echolocation

Two a.m., warm dark on deck
stars dissolving in the hazy sky.
Down below someone murmurs in their sleep.
I put on the headphones
and a shop full of demented clocks explodes into my ears
the tick, tick ticking of a school of sperm whales,
hunting a thousand metres underneath our hull,
finding food with the echo of their voices.
I close my eyes and try to feel what that is like,
Ultrasound maybe?
No. Hearing is their first sense,
they don't need translation to a grainy visual.
They hear, direct, the shape of tentacles, the slippy slime of skin
the insides of things, guts and hearts,
the waxy caverns in the heads of other whales.
Without their clicks the dark around them would seem empty.
Maybe they believe their voices make the world.
If that's what sperm whales think, perhaps we aren't so different
Both of us the centre of our universe.

Scientifically Trained

We were all Scientifically Trained Professionals,
Schooled to Evidence and Observation
Devoted to Data that could be Statistically Tested.
In short, signed up to the whole, stone-cold caboodle of it all.
But when the sperm whale calf swam round our boat,
head out, to look at us,
one way, then the other, clearly fascinated,
we all stood in line waving, calling,
'Hello, whaley!'
knowing that he would understand.

When young male sperm whales begin to leave their mother's social group, they are very curious. The one in this poem, Tram Tracks, lives in the ocean off Dominica and loved to come close to our research boat. I based a novel called Whale Boy *on him.*

The Squid's Mistake

At the surface now, a school of sperm whales takes a rest.

Hunting in the darkness is all done,

As, today, they have a special guest:

A huge old male. Calves and females loll about him in the sun,

Flukes and bellies, fins and heads and jaws

Stick out into the air, as their bendy bodies press him round

They click and click and click without a pause,

A coda storm that fills the swells with happy sound.

Everyone is chilled, until one whale sees a squid close by,

A Humboldt, blood-red against the deepest blue.

The whale is instantly transformed, she's suddenly more vivid,

A focused hunter, like a missile, pursuing, straight and true.

At the surface sperm whales seem as mild as sheep

It's a shock to glimpse their other self, ruthless killer of the deep.

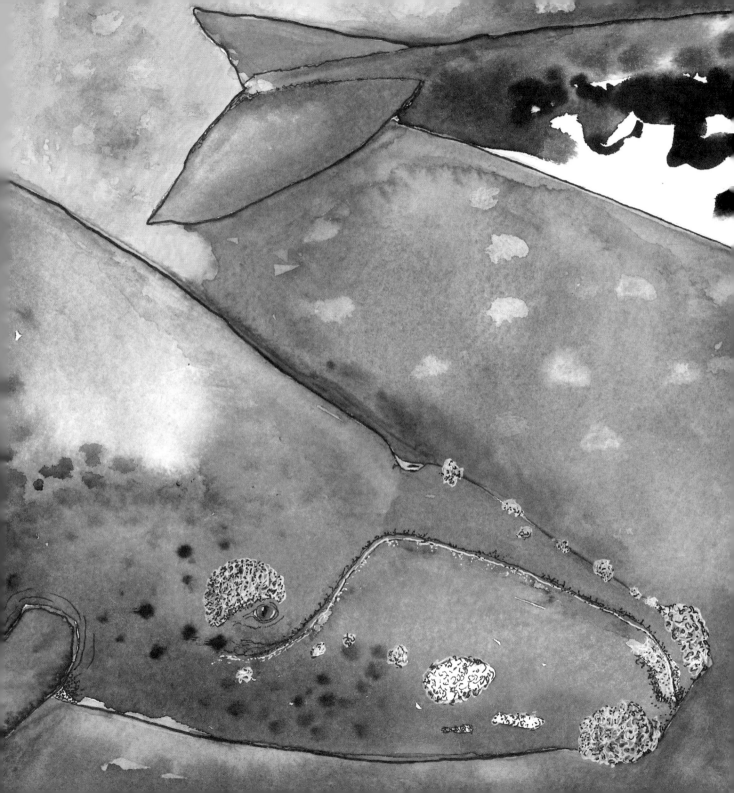

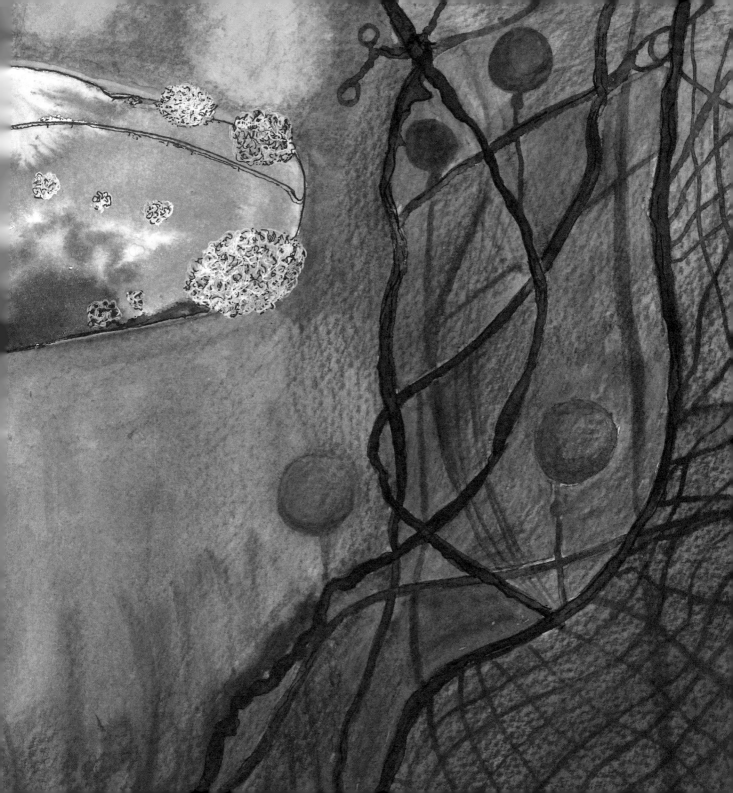

Right Whales

Right whales have the finest baleen of any whale, which means they can filter the smallest creatures from the ocean. Their feeding technique is to swim, very slowly, with their mouths open through swarms of tiny zooplankton.

Their slow speed, their thick blubber and their long baleen plates made them the favourites of whalers, the 'right' whales to hunt. Right whales, like many other baleen whale species, spend half the year feeding in high latitudes then migrate to warmer waters to breed. They tend to stay quite close to land, making them easier for scientists to study, but also bringing them into contact with ships and fishing boats. Although right whales are no longer hunted, they suffer high mortality from collisions with human vessels and entanglement in fishing gear. Two of the three species of right whale, the North Atlantic and North Pacific right whales, are in danger of extinction because of this. They are incredibly lovely animals, emanating a slow, calm energy that you feel the moment you see them.

Whale Catalogue

For Michael Moore, who has spent his life trying to protect North Atlantic right whales from humans.

Scientists give right whales names
Nimbus, Half Note, Pilgrim, Specs.
They log where and when each whale is seen,

This is Juno; she is 38 years old and a mother eight times over.
She and her daughter Limulus both have new born calves this year!

But the log book has a grimmer tale to tell:
the right whales' home is now a shipping lane, a fishing ground
laced with metal hulls like missiles,
propellers, whirring, merciless and sharp,
and endless miles of ropes and gear that trap and snare.

Juno carries scars – a propeller cut her jaw when she was young,
a rope bit deep into her tail; she's missing half a fluke.
Limulus' first child simply vanished.
Nimbus trails three hundred feet of dragging rope;
All eight of Half Note's children died in their first year;
Specs escaped the snare of fishing gear
but is so damaged, he will die;
A rope wrapped Pilgrim's youngest daughter
so her tail was almost severed when she washed up dead.

Whale Catalogue

If we were honest we would rename these whales
to show what they have suffered:

Dragged, Drowned, Tortured,
Starved, Bereaved, Mutilated.

A boat struck Juno's baby.
Its head looks like a rough-sliced loaf.
In the marine motorway that was her world,
Juno tends another dying child.

Right whales have distinctive patterns of rough skin, called callosities, on their head, which allow scientists to identify individuals and to keep track of them over time. There are just 360 North Atlantic right whales left in the world. Of these, only 70 are breeding females.

They share their breeding and feeding grounds with many thousands of human vessels and a high density of fishing gear, which cause very high levels of death and injury. If this continues, North Atlantic right whales will soon be extinct.

Cape Town Whales

It was hard, that day in Cape Town.

In spite of all the sunshine and the coffee shops,

Everything felt wrong and complicated.

There were reports of killings in the papers;

I lost my room key and the car got towed.

So we set off late along the coast

where the shining beaches and the turquoise sea

just made me think of sharks.

We stopped to see the penguins

but they'd caught the vibe:

They huddled miserably under breakwaters

in drifts of moulted feathers, like the end of the world.

And then, quite unexpectedly, whales!

Just here, in the blue beside the highway,

Buoyant as tethered clouds.

We parked up, all askew, and ran to look:

A big, round mother, lovely in her practical, unlovely bulk,

And a calf, ridiculously tiny, at her side

Bobbing, blowing uncertainly, gently bounded by her black flipper.

They floated there together, breathing, being,

And we watched, the mother and her baby

Showing us how simple it could be.

Orcas

Orcas are members of the other half of the cetacean family, the odontocetes, the toothed whales. They are one of the most widespread and successful of all marine species and are rightly known as the 'wolves of the sea'.

They are highly social, living and hunting in stable, well-coordinated groups. In different regions and habitats they have adapted their behaviour to feed on a wide variety of prey using some very clever tricks of the predators trade. There are orca that specialise in tipping seals off ice floes, others that are salmon herders and still others that prey on marine mammals much larger than themselves. The keys to their success as predators are their ability to work together as a team, to teach their young specialised hunting techniques and to innovate. Many other species of whales carry scars on their bodies from orca attacks. Other species fear them, and whenever I have seen them in the wild, other whales are heading in the opposite direction, usually making no sounds so as to slip past the 'sea wolves' undetected. They have a truly heart-stopping magnificence; the sight of them will always make you gasp.

Orcas

All black and white the orca come,
Their tall fins dark against the sun.
They hunt in deadly harmony,
The wildest wolves in all the sea.

They'll swim up from the depths below
To make a wave that tips the floe,
And slides the seal into their jaws,
Then swim away without a pause.
They'll ride a wave right up the beach
To snatch a pup that's out of reach.
They'll bite the tongues of living whales,
Gorge on salmon, leave just scales.
They'll suck the liver from a shark,
In every sea they leave their mark.

All black and white the orca come
Their tall fins dark against the sun.
Like judgement swimming in a line,
Terrible and yet divine.

Winnie

Long ago I rode a killer whale,

She felt just like an egg that's been hard boiled.

She was as captive as a goldfish in a pail,

Her wild life stolen, broken, spoiled.

She carried me around her tiny chlorinated pool,

I was so happy, I didn't think about the cost;

The camera rolled, I grinned just like a fool

And forgot the ocean and the family that she'd lost.

Until I tried to leave and she pulled me back in

She closed her huge mouth around my arm

I felt her teeth, her strength, but she didn't even break the skin.

She was determined, but she didn't mean me harm.

I looked into her eye then, and I could see

She was so lonely, that I was company.

My first job as presenter for the Really Wild Show – *a children's TV programme in the 1980s – was swimming with Winnie, one of the last captive orcas in the UK. She was captured in Iceland in 1977 and lived in a pool in Windsor Safari Park until keeping whales in captivity became illegal in the UK in 1991. She was transferred to Sea World in the US and died in 2002 from problems caused by all the coins and broken tiles she'd swallowed in her pool in Windsor.*

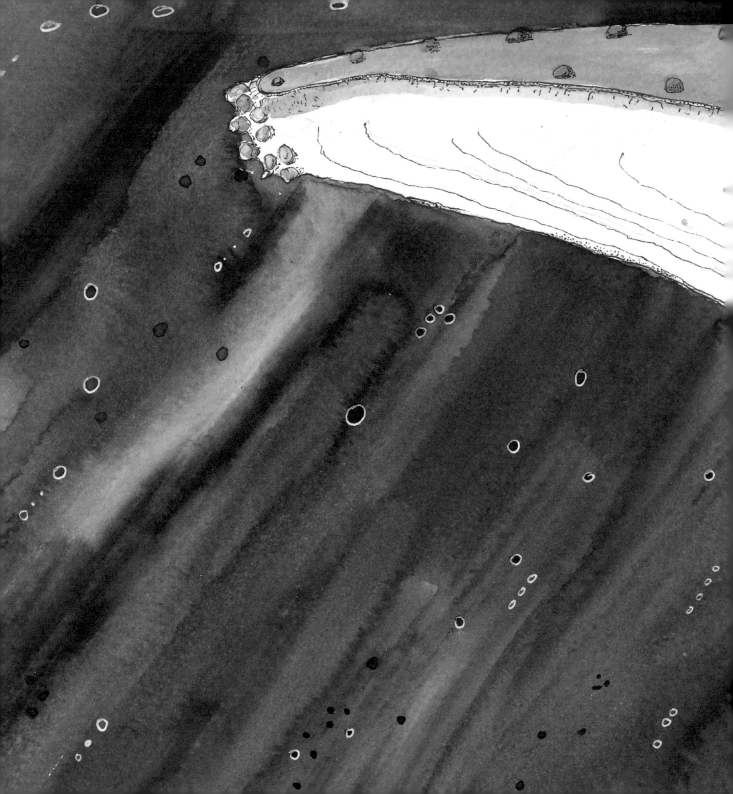

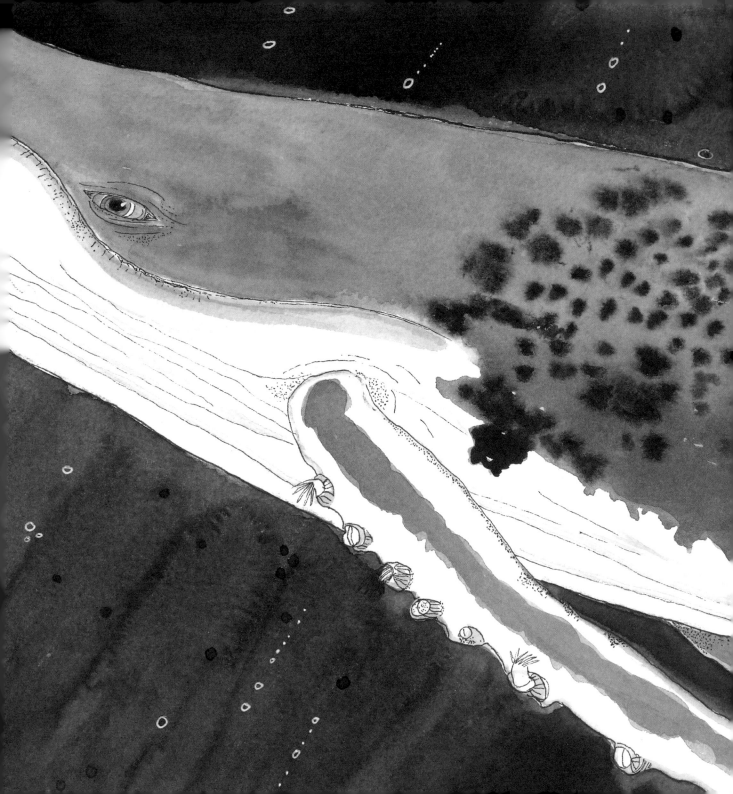

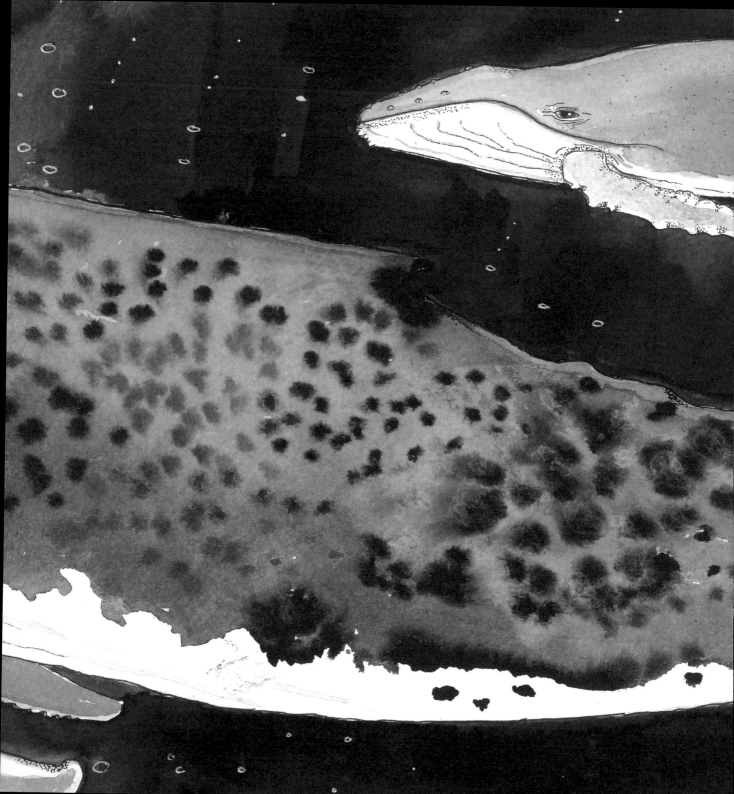

Humpback Whales

Humpbacks are baleen whales like blues, and use their huge mouths and expandable throats to engulf vast numbers of small prey, which they sieve from the water with their baleen plates.

But they have many clever ways of doing this, often working in groups, making huge nets of bubbles to confine prey in dense patches and lunging upwards, mouths open, simultaneously. Like most species of baleen whale, they feed in high latitudes and migrate to warm tropical waters to breed. That's where male humpbacks do their singing. Humpback song is the most complex animal display on the planet. Males in one breeding ground sing the same song, but this changes over time as they compose and improvise and even, occasionally, have song revolutions that completely transform the song that a whole population sings in a few weeks. When I first studied humpbacks, it was on their feeding grounds off the coast of Newfoundland in Canada; I had to wait thirty-seven years to, finally, hear them sing, a sound so transcendently lovely as to be worth every second of that long wait.

First Humpbacks

There were icebergs in the bay too massive and too turquoise to be real
And the village shop sold ship's biscuits instead of bread.
I walked five miles out of town across the empty heath onto the headland
All the plants there were celebrities:
huge, sky-blue irises, dwarf willow winding like a bonkers bonsai
and pitcher plants with blooms more like aliens than flowers.
I put up my tent (twenty quid from my mum's catalogue)
and walked out to the cliff edge.
Dark water and cold wind stretched away to forever;
I wondered how would I do in this odd and wondrous place, alone?
The answer surfaced at the bottom of the cliff: three humpbacks,
the first whales I'd ever, ever seen,
tail stocks delicate as flower stalks behind their flaring flukes
and long white flippers, turquoise as an iceberg in the green sea.

Sea Mist

All that summer, there were sea mists, thick as powdered chalk.

They whipped up from behind the island like a genie summoned from its pot.

At first a tentacle or two and then a fast flood of dead white pouring in,

heavy as milk, to fill the space between the headlands.

A stillness settled then, an intimate calm, like the confessional box.

Invisible behind the screen of fog the whales spoke and breathed

Every nuance transmitted upward by the mist

So I felt that they were whispering straight into my ear.

Fluke Up

At the prow of the boat it's just me and the whale,

the midline of our bodies so aligned,

that her blow feels like my own breath.

She rolls, rolls, rolls forward into her dive.

Her broad back parts the green water, like a polished monument,

huge as a headland;

her move so smooth that time slows and slows and slows

as her knobbled tail stock arches, arches, arches

to lift her flukes free, and holds them,

jewels falling from their gnarly edge –

a giant butterfly of black and white –

against the sky, for one last, long eon of a moment.

*Humpback whales have black and white patterns on the underside of their tails
that are as individually distinct as faces. But these patterns are only visible when
the whales 'fluke up' – lifting their tails above the water before heading down in
an almost vertical dive. This allows scientists a few short seconds to get a tail
shot. Other whales also fluke up and have their tails photographed to help with
identification, but none have patterns as distinct at humpbacks.*

Humpback Singer

Somewhere now a whale is singing
Somewhere out there in the blue
Right now on this spinning planet,
There's a singing whale, and you.

Do you tramp the heartless pavement?
Do you ride the rattling train?
Do you weep under the streetlight,
then lie down and start again?

Then remember now and always
There's another kind of true
And that right now on this planet
There's a singing whale, and you.